THIS BOOK BELONGS TO

Made in United States
North Haven, CT
26 May 2022

19549586R00055